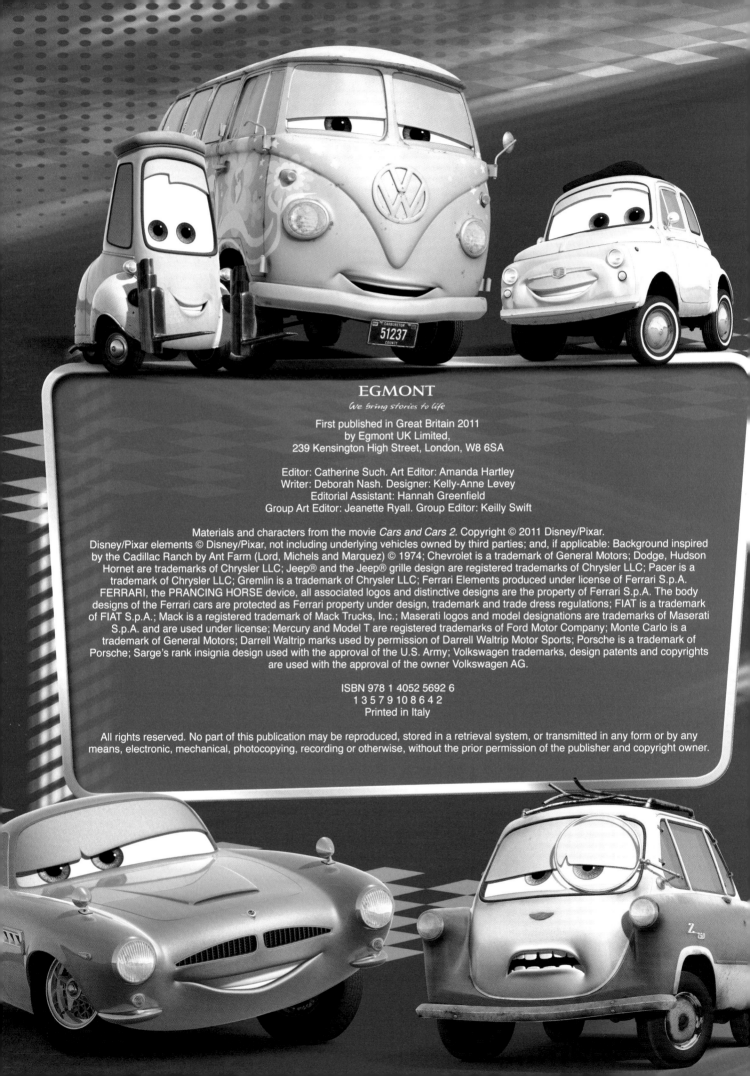

EGMONT
We bring stories to life

First published in Great Britain 2011
by Egmont UK Limited,
239 Kensington High Street, London, W8 6SA

Editor: Catherine Such. Art Editor: Amanda Hartley
Writer: Deborah Nash. Designer: Kelly-Anne Levey
Editorial Assistant: Hannah Greenfield
Group Art Editor: Jeanette Ryall. Group Editor: Keilly Swift

ISBN 978 1 4052 5692 6
1 3 5 7 9 10 8 6 4 2
Printed in Italy

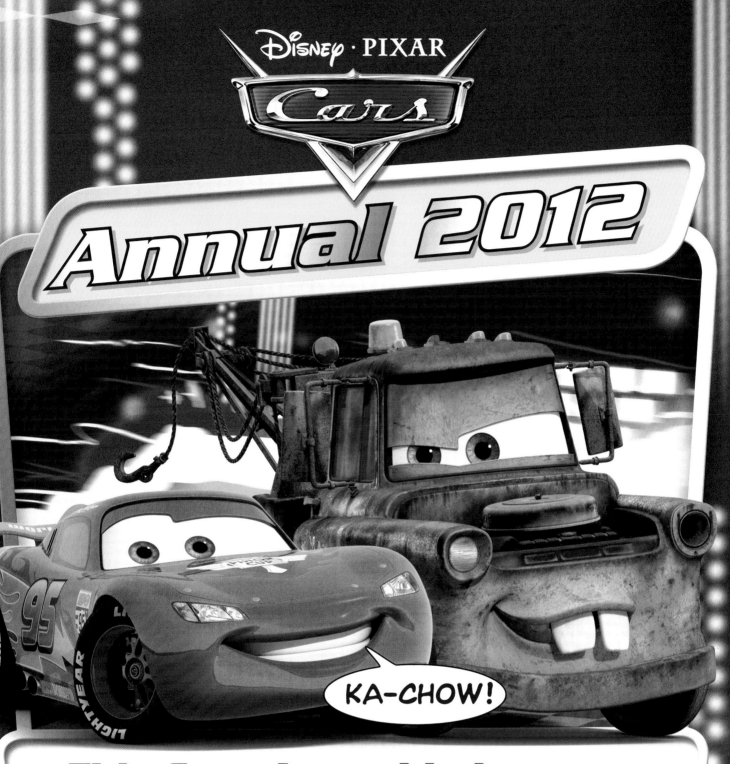

Annual 2012

KA-CHOW!

This Cars Annual belongs to

Name _____ **Age** _____

Favourite Character

_____

Check out the new characters inside!

What's inside?

LET'S GO!

DISNEY·PIXAR

Cars 2

Cars 2 Best Bits

Follow your favourite cars on an adventure around the world! Watch out for nasty Professor Z and the Lemons!

Super Spy

Meet Finn McMissile, British secret agent. He uncovers an evil plot to blow up the race cars in the World Grand Prix competition. He also mistakes Mater for an agent!

Finn McMissile

1 Tokyo Race

First race, Tokyo. Lightning is here with Mater. Finn and his fellow British agent Holley Shiftwell are picking up secret information. It's unlucky their enemy Professor Z is also in town ...

2 The Mission!

An American agent gives Mater the secret information meant for Finn and Holley. The two British spies mistake Mater for the American agent. They ask Mater to help them on their mission.

Lightning

Mater

3 On to Porto Corsa!

The next World Grand Prix race is in Porto Corsa, Italy. There's also a secret meeting taking place there. Mater infiltrates the meeting and discovers that a group of cars called "Lemons" are sabotaging the alternative fuel, Allinol, that the race cars are using.

4 The Warning

During the Porto Corsa race, some of the race cars suffer engine blow-outs and crash. Everyone blames Allinol. But Lightning, who wins the race, says he'll stick with Allinol for the final race in London. Mater finds out that Lightning's life is in danger and tries to warn him. But he, Finn and Holley are captured by the Lemons and tied up in a clock tower in London.

Holley
A beautiful lady secret agent who knows every trick in the spy manual.

Professor Z
He's an evil weapons designer. No racer is safe when he's around.

5 The Escape

Grem and Acer arrive to tell the prisoners that Lightning will be blown up in the next race. Mater escapes, but Holley and Finn realise that HE is carrying the bomb! They break out of the clock tower and head to the London racetrack.

6 London Calling

Finn chases Professor Z down the Thames river and captures him. Holley orders him to deactivate the bomb on Mater, but he can't!

Lemons

Lemons are cars that are faulty. Professor Z's goons are Lemons. The "Lemonheads" are the heads of the four Lemon families.

7 Save the Day

Mater figures out who the "Big Boss" of the Lemons is. The Big Boss is forced to deactivate the bomb and everyone is saved. Mater is the hero!

Read the story on pages 18-21 to find out who the Big Boss is, too!

Secret Mission

1
Finn's Picture Problem

Secret agent Finn McMissile has taken a photograph with his hidden camera but someone has torn it up. Can you put the pieces back in the right order for him?

Finn McMissile is working undercover. Help him solve these puzzles.

a   b

c   d   e   f

Write your answers here! We've done the first one for you.

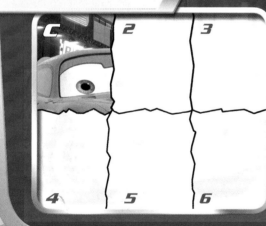

c	2	3
4	5	6

TIME IS OF THE ESSENCE!

2 Headlights On!

Which picture of Mater matches the one here?

Tick the correct box.

Can you find Luigi hidden somewhere on the page?

a

b

c

Wheely Different

Max Schnell and Raoul ÇaRoule are in Tokyo for the first race. Spot the five differences in the bottom picture.

Colour a wheel each time you spot a difference!

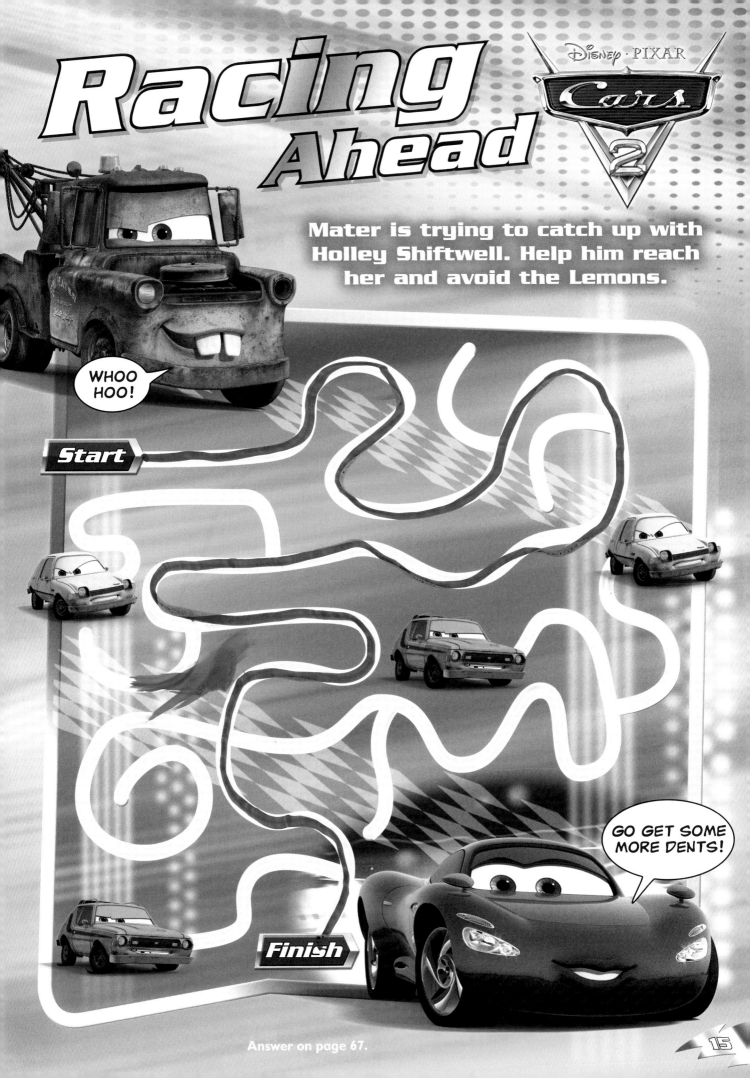

Mystery Motor

Find out who's visiting Uncle Topolino by joining up the dots. Then add some colours.

How many Italian flags can you find hidden on the page?

Answer on page 67.

Grand Finale

Disney · PIXAR Cars 2

It's the World Grand Prix final, but who will win the prize?

How quickly can you put the missing pieces in the right place?

a   b   c   d   e

17

Answers on page 67.

The Story of the Movie

It's evening in Radiator Springs and Mater's watching TV. He learns that Miles Axlerod, former oil baron, is sponsoring the World Grand Prix race where he'll introduce his new alternative fuel, Allinol.

Francesco Bernoulli badmouths Lightning on the same show, so Mater phones in to defend his best friend. But Francesco then turns on Mater, so Lightning rings up! Soon, he's agreed to take part in the World Grand Prix, with Mater as part of the pit crew!

The night before the first race of the World Grand Prix in Tokyo, Lightning and Mater are revving it up at a party. British agents, Finn McMissile and Holley Shiftwell, are at the same party, hoping to meet American secret agent, Rod "Torque" Redline. Due to a strange sequence of events, Torque plants a device on Mater, so Holley thinks that he's the agent!

The Tokyo race starts and it's head-to-head between Lightning and

Slowly Mater starts to connect everything. Finn and Holley are spies! Holley downloads a photo from the device that Torque planted on Mater. The photo is of a mysterious gas-guzzling engine. What did it all mean?

Francesco. Mater's giving Lightning tips on his headset. Holley starts instructing Mater as if he's an agent. Mater inadvertently repeats Holley's instructions to Lightning, who gets confused and loses the race!

Mater feels terrible and decides to head home to Radiator Springs. He doesn't want to make Lightning lose any more races. However, Finn intercepts him at the airport. The two flee from Grem and Acer, two goons who are working for Professor Z, a mad scientist.

They head to Paris, where Finn knows an informant, called Tomber, who works as a spare parts dealer.

It was starting to become clearer. Mater realised that the engine belonged to a "Lemon" – a type of car that always breaks down. Tomber tells them that the Lemons are holding a secret meeting in Porto Corsa, Italy.

all alternative fuels are unsafe, cars will go back to using oil. Since the Big Boss and the Lemons own most of the oil fields, they'll be rich and powerful!

Meanwhile, Finn and Holley realise that Grem and Acer are using a device disguised as a camera to heat up the Allinol fuel and blow up the the engines of race cars. Lightning wins the second Grand Prix race in Porto Corso, but the Lemons vow to destroy him in the final race in London. Mater tries to warn Lightning that his life is in danger, but Mater is kidnapped before he gets a chance.

Mater, disguised as one of the Lemonheads' tow trucks, discovers that they're targeting the racers! The "Big Boss" of the Lemons explains that once they convince everyone that Allinol and

Mater's tied up with Finn and Holley in a clock tower in London. They finally realise that he's not really a spy. Mater manages to escape, determined to save his best friend. But unbeknown to him, he's got a bomb strapped to him!

Finn radios Mater to warn him, but he's already in the pit with Lightning. Mater and Lightning blast off down the streets of London, while Finn heads off to capture Professor Z. Mater works out that the gas-guzzling engine in the photo belongs to Miles Axlerod. Mater heads to Buckingham Palace to tell the Queen that Axlerod is the Big Boss. Axlerod has no choice but to deactivate the bomb and everyone is saved. To thank Mater for his courage, the Queen knights him. Lightning couldn't be more proud of his best buddy.

The End

Say Cheese!

Use your sharp observation skills to answer these questions about the photo.

1

How many cars can you count?

2 Who is the dark red car on the far left?

___ ___ _____ _____

3 Which car has this symbol?

Who has flown into the photo without Lightning realising?

4 Point to the feature on a building that looks like a motor grill.

5 Who are parked by the lamp post in the background?

Answers on page 67.

Who's Who?

Save these eight cars from being cubed by finding their names in the grid.

Lightning

H	S	A	L	L	Y	O	F	H
O	A	L	F	P	M	E	I	S
L	I	G	H	T	N	I	N	G
L	H	K	O	L	I	L	N	A
E	S	L	U	I	G	I	O	T
Y	P	R	N	L	E	M	A	O
A	O	C	A	R	L	A	P	R
M	N	L	R	E	S	M	F	L
T	F	I	L	L	M	O	R	E

Holley

Nigel

Finn

Sally

Luigi

Fillmore

Carla

DON'T GET GRIDLOCKED NOW!

Answers on page 67.

Max's Snaps

Max and Raoul ÇaRoule are racing. Can you spot the details below in the big picture?

a

b

c

d

e

Which one doesn't belong here?

25

Answer on page 67.

All Mixed Up

These cars are in a jumble. Help separate them by answering these questions.

1 Hidden!

This object is hidden in the big picture. Can you find it?

How many pieces come from each car?
Write your answers in the circle.

Carla

Raoul ÇaRoule

Max

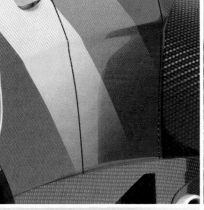

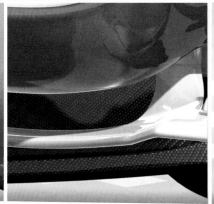

3 Odd One Out

The big picture also contains a piece that doesn't belong to the cars. Can you spot it?

3 Vanishing Act

Someone is disappearing. Can you work out who it is?

4 In a Blur

Can you help Holley Shiftwell work out which car's been blurred out here?

OOPS! THIS PICTURE'S GOT THE WOBBLES!

a

b

c

d

Answers on page 67.

29

The Best of Friends

Can you spot the five differences in the bottom picture of best friends Lightning and Mater?

Colour a road sign every time you find a difference!

Answers on page 67.

Hook and TOW!

Give Mater some cool colours to really make him smile!

I CAN TOW ANYTHING!

DISNEY · PIXAR Cars
Retirement For a Champ

HEY, YOU LOOK LIKE YOU NEED A REST!

The King needs some colour! Can you help him out?

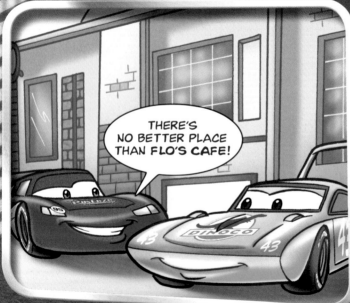

THERE'S NO BETTER PLACE THAN FLO'S CAFE!

A TASTY CAN OF FUEL AND ... EH, WE HAVE VISITORS?

"... LOSING THEM WILL BE **CAR'S PLAY**!"

A LITTLE WHILE LATER ...

I THOUGHT YOU SAID YOU WERE RUSTY? I HAD A HARD TIME **KEEPING UP** WITH YOU!

HEE! HEE! YOU'RE RIGHT! SOME THINGS YOU NEVER FORGET!

BESIDES, A DRIVE THROUGH THE **COUNTRY** IS A FINE WAY TO RELAX!

WATCH OUT!

HUH?

Connect the dots to complete the lost tractor. Then colour him!

AAARGH!

VROOOM

SORRY, GUYS! I DIDN'T MEAN TO SCARE YOU, I WAS FOLLOWING THAT TRACTOR BUT ...

NO PROBLEM, MATER! IT LOOKS LIKE THERE'S ONLY ONE PLACE WHERE I CAN **REALLY** GET SOME REST!

Test Track Qualifiers

Are you a Cars expert? Find out how much you know in the quiz below.

1

What is the name of the hotshot rookie race car?
Use his tattoo flash to help you!

_ _ _ _ _ _ _ _ _ _ _ _ _ _ _

2

How many Piston Cups has The King won?
Colour in the cups to find out.

3

What is Chick Hicks' racing number?

| 43 | 86 | 95 |

4

Where does Luigi work?
Circle the correct answer.

CASA DELLA
TIRES
QUALITY SERVICE

Flo's V8 Cafe

TOW
MATER
TOWING & SALVAGE

a   b    c

5 Who owns the V8 Café in Radiator Springs?
Circle the correct answer.

Flo

Ramone

Doc

6 Mater wakes the tractors by singing a lullaby!

True

False

7 Colour in the dots to find out who this vintage lady is.
Then write her name in the space below!

38

9

Which tattoo belongs to Fillmore?
Add some colour to the correct answer.

a

b

c

d

e

8

Here is Sheriff. Can you spot what's missing from the second picture below?

SHERIFF

SHERIFF

10

What is the name of Lightning's sponsor?

◯ Scratch-eze

◯ Rust-eze

◯ Dent-eze

What's your score?
Colour in your score logo.

8+

Wow! You know your cars, from their seat belts to their wheel tracks! Well done!

5 to 7

You passed the MOT test but you need to polish up on some of your facts to win the cup!

Below 5

Well, if this was a driving test you would be a danger on the roads! Never mind, follow your good friend Mater's example and keep smiling!

An Off Day

ONCE THE POURING RAIN HAD STOPPED ...

NOTHIN' BEATS A GOOD BACKWARDS RACE! YEE-HAA!

HA! HA! HA!

HEE-HEE! HIDING HERE TO SPY ON LIGHTNING MCQUEEN'S MOVES WAS A GREAT IDEA!

SPLASH

86

HEY! WATCH WHERE YOU'RE GOIN' WITH THOSE WHEELS!

OOPS! SORRY!

CHICK?!

What detail is missing from Chick Hicks in this picture?

I'LL LET IT SLIDE THIS TIME!

BUT YOU'RE IN FOR MY NEXT TRICK!

86

Uh-oh! Someone's hiding out to play a trick on Mater. Can you spot where the culprit is?

Answers on page 68.

Colour in Lightning McQueen using the key shown!

SPLOSH!

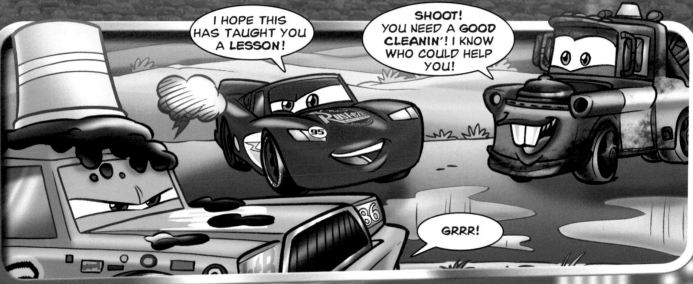

Connect the dots to help Red wash Chick Hicks.

Piston Cup Pile-up

There's a pile-up on the racetrack. Quickly answer these questions before anyone else crashes!

1 How many cars have crashed?

ZOOM

2 What colour is car 76?

purple   yellow

3 Which of the numbers below is written on the blue car?
Tick the correct box.

21   16   95   30   51

Answers on page 68.

Disney · PIXAR
Cars

Team Mates

Join the dots to draw this racer and his helper. Then add colour.

10 11 12 13 14
15
9 16
8 17
7 18
6 19
5 20 24
4 23 25
21 22 26
3 27
2 28 29 30
31
35 34 33 32
36
37
38
39

Can you find the loose tyre hidden on the page?

Lightning's friend has got his name in a muddle. Can you help him by unscrambling the letters?

D G
U
O   I

Write the answer here.

Getting there in Comfort

HEY CHAMP, WHERE ARE YOU? WE NEED YOU FOR OUR NEW RUST-EZE AD CAMPAIGN!

I'M ON MY WAY, CLUNK!

WHAT'S THAT NOISE?

MACK'S STOPPED! LET ME SEE WHAT'S GOIN' ON!

SCREEECH

DO YOU NEED SOME HELP, GUYS?

WE SURE DO! WE'RE ON OUR WAY TO RADIATOR SPRINGS!

VAN TOOK A WRONG TURN AND HE REFUSES TO ASK ANYONE FOR DIRECTIONS ... AS USUAL!

GRUNT! I DON'T NEED ANYONE'S HELP!

NO PROBLEM, WE'LL TELL YOU HOW TO GET THERE!

SEE YOU LATER IN TOWN!

UH-OH! WELL, LOOK WHO'S HERE!

SCREEECH

MINI AND VAN! I FIGURED YOU'D BE IN RADIATOR SPRINGS BY NOW.

DESPITE YOUR DIRECTIONS, WE'VE BEEN DRIVING AROUND **LOST** THE WHOLE DAY!

IT'S NOT MY FAULT! THE ROAD SIGNS ARE WRONG!

SIGH! DO YOU HAVE A MAP WE COULD BORROW?

THAT WON'T BE NECESSARY. WE'RE ON OUR WAY TO RADIATOR SPRINGS RIGHT NOW!

WE CAN TRAVEL TOGETHER!

I CAN MAKE IT THERE **BY** MYSELF!

LATER ...

The End

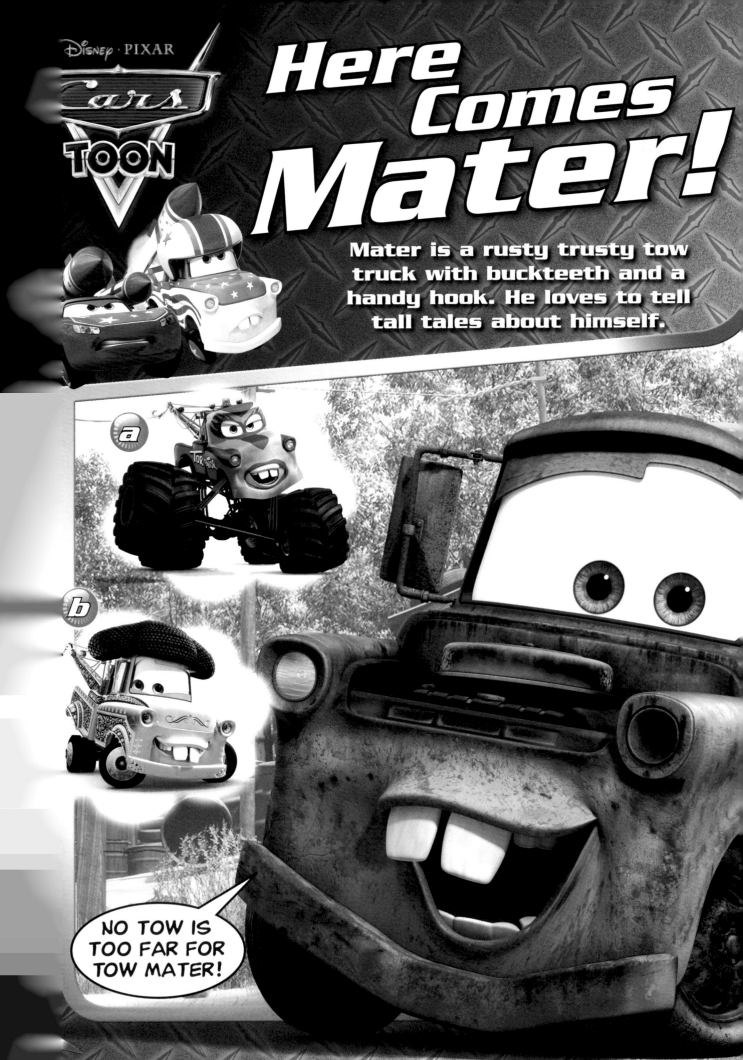

Answers on page 68.

Mater's Daredevil Stunts!

Help Mater the Greater meet the challenges in these puzzles!

T U

T

T

S

N

1 Can you unscramble the letters above to find out what Mater is doing? (There's a clue in the title!)

_ _ _ _ _ _ _

...not come from the picture on the left?

a

b

c

d

e

Which speed trail leads to Mater the Greater?

Answers on page 68.

Mater's Greatest Stunt

WHEN DID YOU LEARN?

SHOOT! THAT WAS YEARS AGO ...

I DON'T KNOW ANYONE WHO CAN DRIVE BACKWARDS LIKE MATER!

ZOOM

"... WHEN I PERFORMED AS **MATER THE GREATER**!"

TODAY, MATER THE GREATER ATTEMPTS HIS **GREATEST STUNT** EVER!

HEE! HEE! I'M GONNA **SHAKE** YOUR SHOCKS, EVERYBODY!

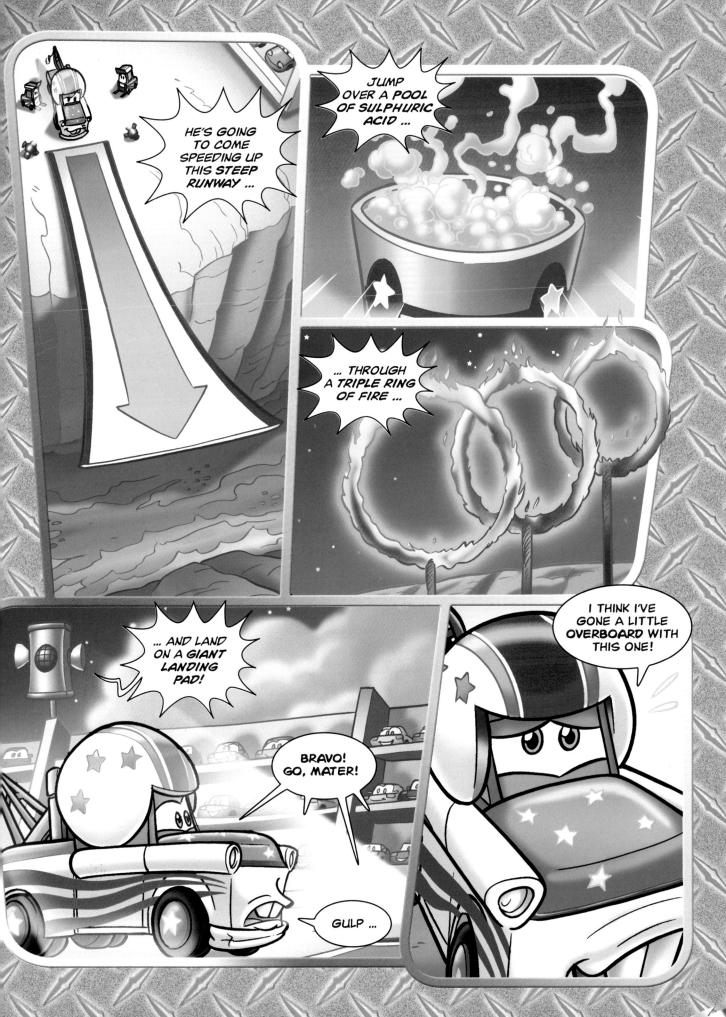

Red Alert!

Rescue Squad Mater's saving Lightning from going up in smoke! Can you spot the five differences in the bottom picture?

Colour a flame every time you find a difference.

YOU CAN COUNT ON ME!

Rock On!

Discover the name of Heavy Metal Mater's band by writing the black letters, in order, in the space below.

Give Heavy Metal Mater's tattoos some colour!

Start

G J S F P E A W C J S T B

DAD GUM!

_ _ _ _ _ _ _ _ _ _ _

Answers on page 67.

6

Make way for El Materdor

El Materdor is fighting bulldozers in Spain. Draw a line from this fearsome bulldozer to his correct shadow.

Can you find a red rose hidden somewhere on the page?

a

b

c

d

OLÉ!

Answers on page 68.

Keeping Score

Find out who Monster Truck Mater is going to fight next. Move forward, left or right, on the squares with this symbol.

Answer on page 68.

Which Mater are You?

Complete this fun quiz to find out which Mater you are most like.

What is your favourite colour?

☐ Red ☐ Black

☐ Blue ☐ Yellow

What do you most like to do?

☐ Race cars ☐ Listen to music ☐ Perform stunts ☐ Dance

Where would you go on a day trip?

☐ Go-cart track ☐ Bowling

☐ Theme park ☐ Pantomine

What is your favourite toy?

Remote control car ☐

Drum kit ☐

Water pistol ☐

Sword ☐

What is your favourite item of clothing?

☐ Chunky trainers ☐ Leather jacket

☐ Superhero cape ☐ Cool hat

Turn over for the results ...

65

Mostly red
You are lively and full of energy, just like Monster Truck Mater. There's never a dull moment with you around!

Mostly black
You and Heavy Metal Mater both love making noise! You like to be noticed and stand out from the crowd.

Mostly yellow
You and El Materdor could be twins! You both love being the centre of attention and having lots of fun.

Mostly blue
You are brave and adventurous, just like Mater the Greater. You love performing tricks and stunts!

If you ticked lots of different colours, you're an awesome mix of Maters!

Answers

Page 12

Secret Mission

1 The pieces are in the following order:
1 - c, 2 - f, 3 - a, 4 - d, 5 - b, 6 - e.
2 c.
Luigi is hidden in the title box.

Page 14

Wheely Different

Page 15

Racing Ahead

Page 16

Mystery Motor

There are 7 Italian flags hidden on the page.

Page 17

Grand Finale

a - 3, b - 5, c - 2, d - 4, e - 1.

Page 22

Say Cheese!

1 There are 6 cars (including the car statue).
2 Uncle Topolino.

3 Fillmore.
5 Guido and Luigi are parked by the lamp post.
Finn McMissile has flown into the photo as a plane.

Page 24

Who's Who?

Page 25

Max's Snaps

Piece 'c' doesn't belong in the big picture.

Page 26

All Mixed Up

2 Raoul ÇaRoule - 5, Carla - 5, Max - 6.
3 The red piece in the bottom row doesn't belong to the cars.

Page 28

Car Parts

1 Car A.
2 Tokyo.
3 Luigi is disappearing.
4 Car 'd' has been blurred out.

Page 30

The Best of Friends

More Answers

Page 35

Retirement for a Champ

Logo 3 is the correct Dinoco logo.

Page 36

Test Track Qualifiers

1 Lightning.

2 7 cups.

3 86.

4 a - Casa Della Tires.

5 Flo owns the V8 Café.

6 False. Mater wakes the tractors with a loud toot!

7 The vintage car is Lizzie.

8

9 Tattoo 'c' belongs to Fillmore.

10 Rust-eze.

Page 40

An Off Day

The number 86 is missing from Chick's side.

Chick is hiding behind the Tire Repair sign.

Page 44

Piston Cup Pile-up

1 5 cars have crashed.

2 Car 76 is purple.

3 The blue car is 51.

4 Zoom.

Page 46

Team Mates

The loose tyre is behind the bush.

Lightning's friend is Guido.

Page 52

Here Comes Mater!

1 - a, 2 - d, 3 - e, 4 - c, 5 - b.

Page 54

Mater's Daredevil Stunts

1 Stunt.

2 Piece 'd' does not belong to the picture.

3 Trail 'b' leads to Mater the Greater.

Page 60

Red Alert!

Page 61

Rock on!

Heavy Metal Mater's band was called Gas Caps.

Page 62

Make Way for El Materdor

Shadow 'b' is correct.
The rose is in El Materdor's mouth.

Page 63

Keeping Score